THE MUSIC OF MICHEL LEGRAND

Although the arrangements of the
Michel Legrand numbers in this book are
for piano, the publishers would like to
acknowledge the following lyric writers
whose words helped make these melodies
such a memorable success.

Marilyn and Alan Bergman for the lyrics of:
Ask Yourself Why
His Eyes, Her Eyes
I Will Say Goodbye
One At A Time
One Day
Pieces Of Dreams
The Summer Knows
Sweet Gingerbread Man
What Are You Doing The Rest Of Your Life
The Windmills Of Your Mind

Hal Shaper for the lyrics of:
I Still See You
Paris Was Made For Lovers
A Place In Paris
Sea And Sky
The Years Of My Youth
Touch The Sun

Norman Gimbel for the lyrics of:
I Will Wait For You
Watch What Happens

Wise Publications
London/New York/Sydney/Tokyo/Cologne

Exclusive distributors:
Music Sales Limited
78 Newman Street, London W1P 3LA, England.
Music Sales Pty. Limited
27 Clarendon Street, Artarmon, Sydney, NSW 2064, Australia.

This book ©Copyright 1979 by
Wise Publications
ISBN 0.86001.703.6
Order No. AM 25727

Designer: Mike Bell

Music Sales complete catalogue lists thousands
of titles and is free from your local music
book shop, or direct from Music Sales Limited.
Please send 30p in stamps for postage to
Music Sales Limited, 78 Newman Street, London W1P 3LA.

Printed in England by
The Camelot Press Limited, Southampton

Moderato (with expression)

Bb9(sus 4)

Ebmaj7

Fm7

Gm7

C11

Abmaj7

Db9(5b)

Gm7   Eb9

C11

Fm7

Bb11

Ebmaj7

Bb11

Ebmaj

Bb11

cresc.

f

dim.

mf

dim. poco a poco

rall.

p

Ebmaj7

Bb11

Ebmaj7

HIS EYES, HER EYES

MICHEL LEGRAND

Moderately Slow with Expression

Gm7

Gmaj7

Gm7

Gmaj7

Gm7(Dbass)   D7[+5][b5]

Gmaj7   *tacet - - - - - ** C#m7

F#7(b9)

Bmaj7

Cm7

F7(b9)

Bbmaj7

Bm7

E7(b9)

Amaj7

9

F

G6

G6

F/G   G6   F/G   Tacet_____ *

D. S. al Coda   ⊕ *CODA*

Tacet_____ *   C6

Ab7   Dm7   Dbmaj7   C$^{6}_{9}$

Moderately

C#m   E/B   F#m   A/E   Bsus   B7

E7   Em7   E

Em7   Bm

G   B   G

Bm/F#   Esus   Esus

21

ff

A   A/G♯

D/F♯   E7   A   A/G♯   D/F♯   E7

A   A/G♯   D/F♯   A/E   G/D   D

Esus   E   E7   A   A/G♯   D/F♯   E7

A   A/G♯   A11   A7   Dmaj7

A/C#   Bm7   Esus E7

A A/G# D/F# E/G# A A/G#

D/F# E/G# A A/G# D/F# A/E

molto Rall. *tempo Rubato*

D A/C# Bm7 E11 E A

dim. *poco a poco*

G   Fmaj7   Amaj7

I STILL SEE YOU

MUSIC BY MICHEL LEGRAND

Moderately with feeling

Am   Am(7#)   Am7   Am6   Fmaj7

Dm7   Bm7   E7
       (5♭)

Amaj7   Tacet_____* Bm7   E9
                        (5♭)

Amaj7   A6   Bm7   E7   Amaj7
               (5♭)

A♭m7   D♭7   G♭maj7   G♭   Gm7   C7
        (9♭)   (9♭)

ONE AT A TIME

MUSIC BY

MICHEL LEGRAND

Chorus

Ebmaj7   Eb6   F9   Cm7   F9

Fm7   Bb9   Fm7   Bb7   Ebmaj7   Emaj7   Fmaj7   Emaj7

Ebmaj7   Eb6   F9   Cm7   F9

Fm7   Bb9   Fm7   Bb7   Ebmaj7   Emaj7   Fmaj7   Gbmaj7

Gmaj7   Fmaj7 Gb Gmaj7 Tacet_____* Gm7   C9   Gm7   C9
                       maj7

D(sus4)   D   Bm7   Em7

Bm7   Em   Em7   C   G (Ped B)   Am11

D11   B(sus4)   B   B(sus4)   B

1   *To Coda* ⊕

C   G (Ped B)   Am11   D11   G   G11

Gmaj7   Am7   A♭9   G   Bm   Em   Em7

PIECES OF DREAMS

MUSIC BY MICHEL LEGRAND

Bm9   E7   C#m7   F#7

B   Bmaj7   Bm7   E7   A   A/G#

F#m   C#m   F#m   C#m   B11   E7   Amaj7

Dmaj7/A   Em7   Amaj7

rall

Bm9   E7   A

8ve

Ped

49

THE SUMMER KNOWS

MICHEL LEGRAND

Slowly with expression

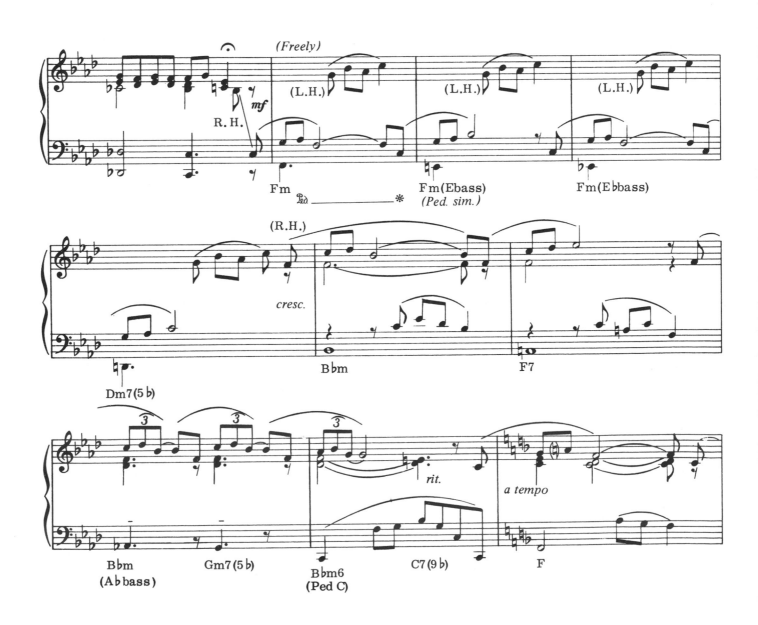

B♭m6(Fbass)   F   Cm7(Fbass)   B♭maj7

Bm7(5♭)   E7   E7(9♭)   Amaj7   E7(9♭)   Amaj7   E♭7(9♭)   A♭maj7   E♭7(9♭)

A♭maj7   D7(9♭)   G   Gm7(5♭)   F

B♭m6(Fbass)   F(Cbass)   B♭m6(Cbass)   Fm6(Cbass)

dim.

B♭m6(cbass)   Fm   Fm9(7♯)

pp